One day Kevin and Lotty are

going to play on the rocks.

They go down the road until they

come to a gate.

1

'Moo ... moo ... moo.' Oh no!

A brown cow is on the grass

behind the hedge.

'Moo ... moo ... moo.'

2

Kevin does not like cows. He will
not go past it. So the little dogs
keep going down the road.

They come to a gap in the

hedge. They can see the rocks.

'Let's run to the rocks,' says

Lotty.

'Grrr ... grrr ... grrr.'

A big brown dog is behind the

hedge. 'Grrr ... grrr... grrr.'

Kevin does not like big dogs.

He will not go past the big brown

dog. So the little dogs keep going

down the road.

Soon they come to some trees.

They can see the rocks.

'Let's run to the rocks,' says

Lotty.

7

'Whoo, whoo, whoooooooo.'

A brown owl comes down from

a tree. Kevin runs away.

Lotty is cross with Kevin now.

She runs off to the rocks to have

fun by herself.

Kevin sits down on the grass. He
sees a brown cow, a brown dog
and a brown owl. Oh no! What
will Kevin do now?

'ow'

cow

now

down

brown

owl

soft 'g'

hedge

Other Vocabulary:

Phase 2:   on a is not dogs gap in can run big off fun and rocks let's sits it

Phase 3:   will with Kevin

Phase 4:   past from cross grass

Vowel Digraphs:

ay: day play says away (gate)

ee: see trees keep

oo: moo soon

oa: road

Tricky words:

to the go no he she they are have one some come little what oh so do does going like by herself

Others:

Lotty behind until gate